TopReaders

more Nonfiction Reading Comprehension

D1469399

This book belongs to

....

Kate McAllan

Contents

Special Silk

Read about these beautiful kites that were made long ago in China. If you come across any new words, sound them out.

In ancient China, silk was expensive. Rich people dressed in silk clothes when they were in public. At home, they wore less costly garments. Rich Chinese women often wore silk shoes. Poorer people wore clothes made of rougher cloth, such as hemp.

Tapestries are woven pictures. Chinese artists wove colored silk threads into tapestries. They also painted on silk cloth. Scenes from nature were popular.

People in ancient China loved to make and fly kites. At first, kites were made of bamboo covered with colorful silk. Later, paper was used to make the kites. It was lighter than silk.

1 Are these sentences True or False? Color in the star next to the correct answer.

(a) Pictures of rivers and mountains were often painted on silk cloth.

☆ True   ☆ False

(b) Rich Chinese women often wore shoes made of hemp.

☆ True   ☆ False

(c) Only rich people could afford to wear silk clothes.

☆ True   ☆ False

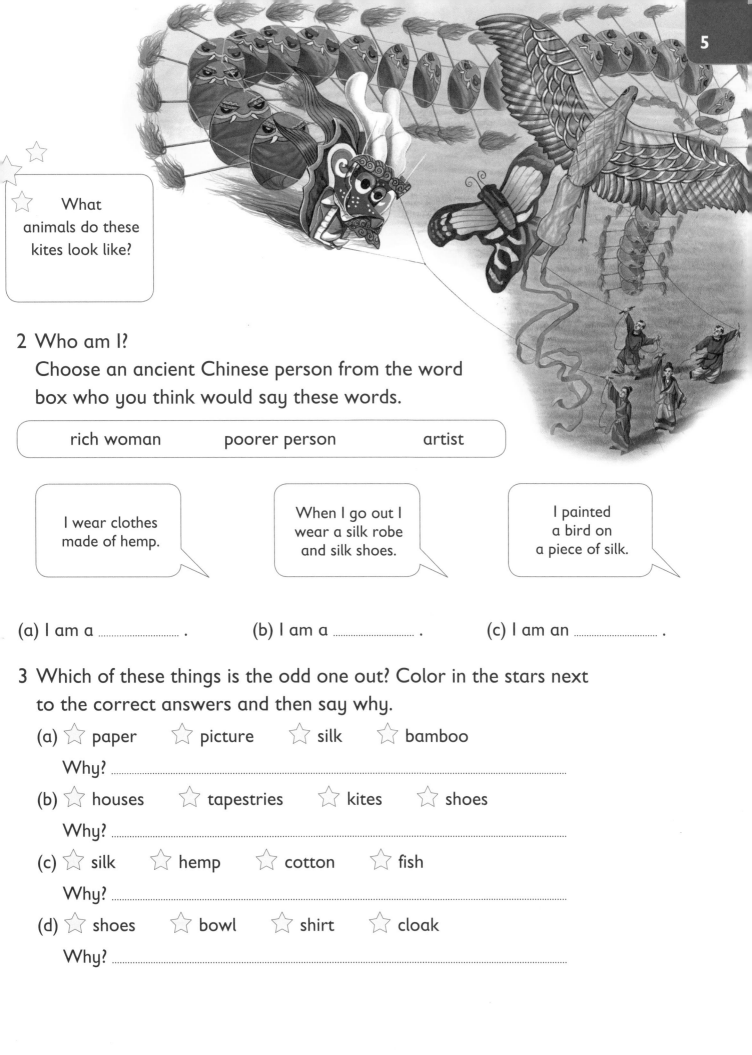

What animals do these kites look like?

2 Who am I?

Choose an ancient Chinese person from the word box who you think would say these words.

| rich woman | poorer person | artist |

I wear clothes made of hemp.

When I go out I wear a silk robe and silk shoes.

I painted a bird on a piece of silk.

(a) I am a ....

(b) I am a ....

(c) I am an ....

3 Which of these things is the odd one out? Color in the stars next to the correct answers and then say why.

(a) ☆ paper   ☆ picture   ☆ silk   ☆ bamboo

Why? ....

(b) ☆ houses   ☆ tapestries   ☆ kites   ☆ shoes

Why? ....

(c) ☆ silk   ☆ hemp   ☆ cotton   ☆ fish

Why? ....

(d) ☆ shoes   ☆ bowl   ☆ shirt   ☆ cloak

Why? ....

Fire down Below

Did you know that lava is melted rock? Find out more in this story. Use a dictionary to find the meaning of new words. Try the word puzzles, too.

Deep beneath Earth's surface, the heat melts rocks. The melted rock, called magma, flows upward. If the magma goes up through the cracks in Earth's surface, it can form volcanoes.

When magma reaches the top of a volcano, it can spurt high into the air as lava. Gases and hot ash form thick, dark clouds. The lava flows down the mountainside. As it cools, it forms new rock.

In a volcanic eruption, most of the lava flows out of the crater. In some cases, magma may rise through channels that force their way out through a side vent.

1 Answer these questions about the story.

(a) What comes out of a volcano during an eruption?

....

(b) Where does most lava come out of a volcano?

....

(c) How does magma escape from inside Earth?

....

2 Draw a line from each word to its meaning.

magma   a mountain pushed up from Earth's surface by magma and gas

lava   a wide, bowl-shaped opening at the top of a volcano

volcano   magma that has come out of a volcano

crater   hot, melted rock

3 Search the word puzzle for the words in the list below
and circle them.

ASH
CHANNELS
CRACKS
CRATER
EARTH
LAVA
MAGMA
MELTED
MOUNTAIN
SURFACE
UPWARD
VENT

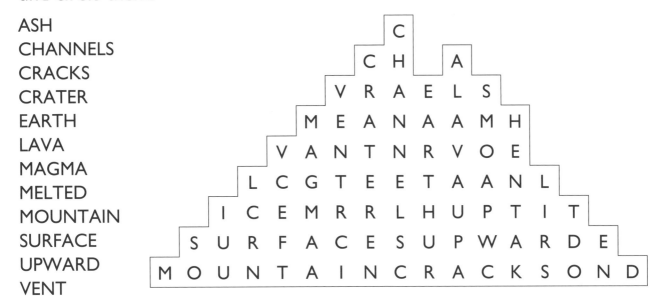

```
                    C
                C   H       A
                V   R   A   E   L   S
            M   E   A   N   A   A   M   H
        V   A   N   T   N   R   V   O   E
        L   C   G   T   E   E   T   A   A   N   L
    I   C   E   M   R   R   L   H   U   P   T   I   T
S   U   R   F   A   C   E   S   U   P   W   A   R   D   E
M   O   U   N   T   A   I   N   C   R   A   C   K   S   O   N   D
```

4 There are **16** letters that have not been circled. Use the leftover letters
to make this mystery phrase:

……. ……. ……. ……. ……. ……. ……. …….   ……. ……. ……. ……. ……. ……. ……. …….

What color
is the lava
in this picture?

Busy Beetles

Did you know that there are beetles that eat dung?
Read about them in this story. Then try the fun activities
to see how much you've learned.

There are hundreds of thousands of different kinds of beetles.
These insects have thicker shells than those of other insects.
Their two front wings are hard. They cover and protect the
soft back wings that beetles use to fly.

  Some beetles eat plants. Others, such as ladybugs, hunt small
animals. Adult dung beetles feed on the juices in animal droppings,
as well as on mushrooms and rotting leaves.

  Dung beetles roll animal droppings into balls and bury them.
Female dung beetles lay eggs inside pieces of dung. When the
beetle larvae hatch, they feed on the dung.

1 Finish these sentences. Color in the star next to the correct answer.

(a) Beetles have hard front wings that ....

  ☆ protect the wings they use to fly.

  ☆ help them fly in strong winds.

(b) Female dung beetles lay their eggs ....

  ☆ on rotting leaves.

  ☆ in pieces of animal dung.

(c) After they roll animal droppings into balls,
dung beetles often ....

  ☆ bury the balls under the ground.

  ☆ store the balls in cracks in tree bark.

2 Here is an example of a word ladder. It takes two steps to turn the word "wall" into the word "tail."
Only one letter can be changed each row.

wall—change one letter (w to t)
tall—change one letter (l to i)
tail—Hooray!

w	a	l	l
t	a	l	l
t	a	i	l

Now it's your turn. Change the word "back" into the word "dung." Fill in the table with the words.

b	a	c	k
d	u	n	g

3 Can you help the dung beetle find its way through the maze to get to its home?

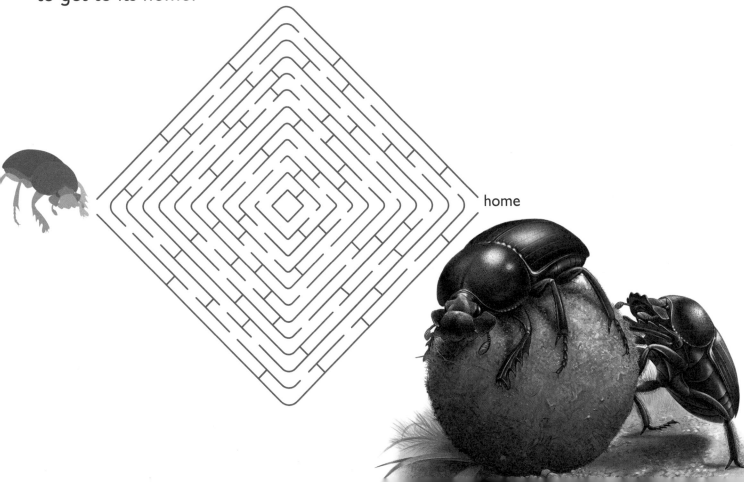

home

Fire and Heat

Read this story about how fire was used to make metal. Have fun completing the activities and word puzzles when you finish reading the story.

When things burn, they give off energy as heat and light. Early people learned to make fire and then used it to cook food, to keep warm, and to give light.

Around 9,000 years ago, fire was first used to bake clay pots. Then, about 8,000 years ago, hotter fires were used to make the first metal objects.

In ancient Egypt, people made metal by heating ore in clay pots. Ore is soil and rock that contain metal elements. To make the fire hot enough to change the ore to metal, they blew onto it through reeds tipped with clay.

1 Complete the sentences by choosing the correct word. Circle your answers.

(a) Early people used fire to ..clean / cook.. their food and keep them warm / cheerful..

(b) Fire was used to ..bake / break / blast.. clay pots long before it was used to make ..metal / light..

(c) Ancient Egyptians made fires ..hotter / smaller.. by ..fanning / blowing.. on them.

2 Rearrange the letters in these words to make words from the story.

(a) lacy   ....

(b) rife   ....

(c) oils   ....

(d) spot   ....

3 Match the jigsaw parts to make sentences. Use different colors to match the sentence parts.

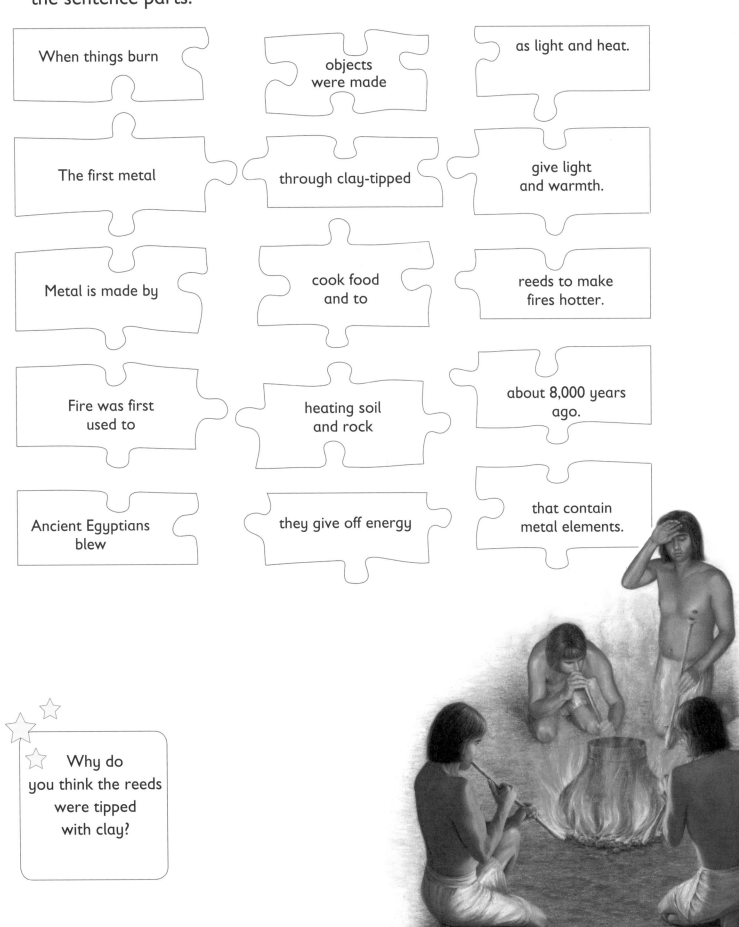

When things burn	objects were made	as light and heat.
The first metal	through clay-tipped	give light and warmth.
Metal is made by	cook food and to	reeds to make fires hotter.
Fire was first used to	heating soil and rock	about 8,000 years ago.
Ancient Egyptians blew	they give off energy	that contain metal elements.

Why do you think the reeds were tipped with clay?

Travel on the Wing

Read about the long journey Arctic terns make each year.
If you find a new word, look at the words around it to help
work out its meaning.

Every year, Arctic terns breed in the far north of the world.
The female tern lays one or two eggs in a dip on the ground.
Both males and females care for the chicks.

At the end of the northern summer, the terns leave. They fly all the
way to near the South Pole. When the southern summer finishes, they
fly north again. Each year, they travel farther than any other animal.

Arctic terns are fantastic fliers. They have a streamlined body and
long, narrow wings. They use their forked tail to change direction
quickly. During their long flight, they feed on fish.

1 Here are some questions about the story.
  Color in the star next to each correct answer.

(a) Where do Arctic terns lay their eggs?

☆ Arctic terns make their nests in tall palm trees.

☆ They lay their eggs on the ground in shallow hollows.

☆ Arctic terns lay their eggs in piles of dried seaweed.

(b) Where do Arctic terns fly to after they have raised their chicks?

☆ Arctic terns fly to Africa at the end of winter.

☆ These terns fly to the far northern part of the world.

☆ They fly to near the South Pole, where it is summer.

(c) What do Arctic terns eat on their long flights?

☆ They eat fish that they catch in the ocean.

☆ They stop to rest and pick sea creatures from the mud.

☆ They do not eat at all and live on fat stored in their body.

2 A word that means the same as another word is called a synonym.
Choose a synonym for each of these words. Circle the correct answer.

(a) finishes

> swallows　　　　ends　　　　goes

(b) dip

> hollow　　　　soar　　　　change

(c) narrow

> thin　　　　long　　　　swift

3 Here's a fun crossword. The answers are words in the story.

Across
1. Comes to an end. (8 letters)
4. A type of sea bird. (4)
5. A greater distance. (7)
6. A young bird. (5)

Down
2. The hottest season of the year. (6)
3. The region in the far north of the world. (6)
4. To go on a journey. (6)

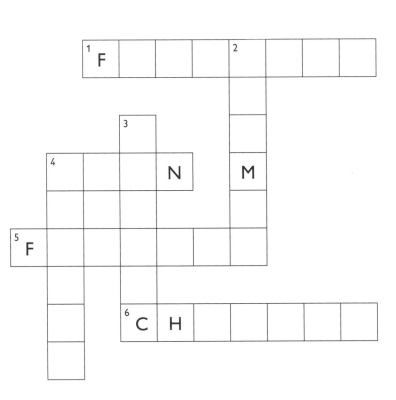

Cycles of Speed

Read about bicycle races. Use a dictionary to find the meaning of new words. Try the word puzzles, too.

Some bicycle races are held in velodromes. Here cyclists speed around tracks inside large stadiums. Other, longer, cycling races take place on public roads. Some of them take days, or even weeks, to complete.

The Tour de France is a famous road cycle race. It was first held in 1903. It is run every July. Riders in the Tour de France travel about 2,500 miles (4,000 km) in three weeks. The most difficult part of the race is through the Pyrenees Mountains in southwestern France. The rider who is coming first wears a yellow jersey.

1 Answer these questions about the story.

(a) Where are long-distance cycle races held?

....

(b) In what year was the Tour de France first held?

....

(c) When is the Tour de France held every year?

....

2 Draw a line between the sentences that have the same meaning.

The Tour de France is held over three weeks.	The cyclist who is winning wears a yellow jersey.
The Tour de France is held on public roads.	It takes 21 days to complete the Tour de France.
The yellow jersey is worn by the rider coming first in the race.	Cars normally travel on roads where the Tour de France is run.

3 Look at the picture. Color in the star next to the things you can see.

☆ yellow jersey ☆ book ☆ mountains ☆ monkey ☆ flags

☆ crowds ☆ motorcycle ☆ cyclists ☆ river ☆ skyscrapers

4 Now pretend you are covering the story for a newspaper.
Write a short report.

Tour de France

....

....

....

....

....

☆ Why are
the cyclists
wearing helmets?

Undersea Exploring

Who are *Alvin* and *Jason Junior*? You'll find out when you read this story about submersibles. Complete the fun activities when you finish reading the story.

Submersibles are small submarines. A submersible can go deeper than a larger submarine. It can take scientists down to explore the ocean depths. Some submersibles are controlled by robots. They don't have people in them. These very small machines can reach places that larger submersibles cannot get to.

   The submersible in this picture is called *Alvin*. It takes people almost 15,000 feet (4,600 m) under the sea's surface. It has lights, cameras, and robotic arms for collecting samples. *Alvin* carries a smaller submersible called *Jason Junior*. This robot takes photos in places where it is too dangerous for *Alvin* to go.

1 Are these sentences True or False? Color in the star next to the correct answer.

(a) All submersibles are controlled using only robots.

☆ True   ☆ False

(b) Submersibles cannot carry people.

☆ True   ☆ False

(c) *Alvin* can go almost 15,000 feet (4,600 m) under the surface of the sea.

☆ True   ☆ False

2 Unscramble these words to make sentences. Don't forget to use capital letters and periods.

(a) can ocean into deep the submersibles very go

....

(b) submersibles using collect scientists samples

....

(c) submersibles some control robots

....

3 Here's a fun crossword.
The answers are words in the story.

Across
4. Things that take photographs. (7 letters)
6. The opposite of safe. (9)
7. The outside of something. (7)
8. A kind of boat that can travel under water. (9)

Down
1. Bits of something that show what the whole thing is like. (7)
2. A small kind of submarine. (11)
3. People who work in a field of science. (10)
5. A machine that can do some of the work a person can. (5)
6. The deep parts of the ocean. (6)

One World

Read this story to learn about the seven continents. To find out what countries are in each continent look at an atlas or a globe of the world.

About two-thirds of Earth's surface is covered by water. One-third is land. The large areas of land between the oceans are called continents. There are seven continents. They are Europe, North America, South America, Asia, Africa, Australia, and Antarctica.

Europe and Asia are joined. Together, they form one landmass. But we always describe them as two continents because their lands and peoples are so different from each other.

The continents haven't always been where they are now. Earth's surface is made up of vast sheets of rock called tectonic plates. These plates slowly move, so the continents do as well.

1 Answer these questions about the story.

(a) How much of our planet is covered by land?

....

(b) How many continents are there?

....

(c) Why do the continents move?

....

a   b   c   d   e   f   g   h   i   j   k   l   m

2 A code is a system of signals or symbols used to send messages.
In this code, numbers stand for letters.

Use the alphabet at the bottom of the page to help you work out the code.
g = 20, h = 19, i = 18, and so on

Now use the code to work out this message.

26 8 18 26   18 8   7 19 22

....

25 18 20 20 22 8 7   24 12 13 7 18 13 22 13 7.

....

3 Use the letters of the word "PLATES"
to fill in this sudoku. Each letter
appears once in each line across and
down, and once in each mini-grid.

E	L	A		P	T
P			L	A	
A	T				L
T	E			L	S
				T	
		S			P

☆
☆
☆ Which continent is farthest south?

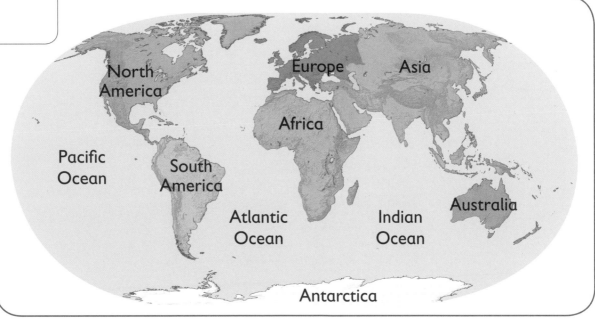

North America
Europe
Asia
Africa
Pacific Ocean
South America
Atlantic Ocean
Indian Ocean
Australia
Antarctica

n o p q r s t u v w x y z

Aztec and Mayan Crafts

Read about the things the Aztecs and Maya made.
Use a dictionary to find the meaning of new words.
Try the word puzzles, too.

Aztec and Mayan craft workers made pots, stone statues, masks, and jewelry. They used colorful feathers to create spectacular cloaks and headdresses.

A carved Aztec mortar, or stone dish, and pestle, or grinder, is shown on page 21. It was used to grind chilies and other plants to use in cooking.

Pots, like the one shown on page 21, were molded from clay by hand. The pots were painted.

The top mask on page 21 is made of gold. Masks were also made from wood and jade. When rulers and other powerful people died, they were often buried with masks over their faces and fine pots beside them.

1 Read the questions, then color in the star next to each correct answer.

(a) What did the Aztecs and Maya use feathers to make?

☆ They used feathers to make soft blankets for babies.

☆ They used feathers to make magnificent headdresses.

(b) What were masks often used for?

☆ Masks were often put over the faces of important people when they were buried.

☆ Masks were often worn during plays put on to entertain important people.

(c) What were the mortar and pestle shown here used for?

☆ They were used to grind chilies and other plant foods.

☆ They were used to grind gold to be made into paint.

2 A word that means the opposite of another word is called an antonym. Choose an antonym for each of these words. Circle the correct answer.

(a) spectacular

> dull   useful   brilliant

(b) powerful

> loud   unimportant   joyful

(c) create

> destroy   polish   make

(d) died

> ate   slept   lived

3 Draw a line from the things to what the story says they are made from.

mask	clay
cloak	gold
statue	feathers
pot	stone

golden Aztec mask

mortar and pestle

clay pot

Mayan death mask

Pictures in the Sky

Find out about how people made up the constellations.
Then try the fun activities to see how much you have learned.

People have been looking at the Sun, Moon, planets, and stars for thousands of years. Early skywatchers picked out groups of stars that they saw as patterns. These groups of stars are called constellations.

To early skywatchers, the sky was a magical place. They saw constellations as animals and gods. They gave the constellations names such as Leo the lion, Cancer the crab, Gemini the twins, and Taurus the bull.

People thought the movements of the constellations made things happen on Earth. They tracked the stars and made star charts to try to predict what would happen in the future.

1 Complete each sentence by choosing the correct word.
Circle your answers.

(a) Patterns of ..stars / moons.. in the sky are called
..installations / constellations..

(b) Long ago people ..thought / dreamed.. that patterns of stars were
..monsters / gods..

(c) People watched the ..makers / movements.. of stars and made star
..charts / models..

2 Who are we?

Use the clues to name the constellations.

> I roar and have a mane.

> There are two of us. We look the same as each other.

> I have a hard shell and two claws.

(a) I am ....

(b) I am ....

(c) I am ....

3 Use these clues to find smaller words made by letters in the word "constellation."

(a) People living together as a country.

..n.. ....n..

(b) A place where passengers get on and off a train.

....i.. ..o.. ....

(c) One hundred of these make up one dollar.

....e.. ....

(d) The opposite of early.

....

(e) An idea or belief.

....o.. ..t.. ..i.. ....

(f) To throw something.

..c.. ....t..

 Are all the stars in the sky used to make constellations?

Don't Eat Me!

Why shouldn't anything eat these frogs? Find out by reading the story below. Then enjoy completing the fun activities.

Some animals are poisonous to eat. They usually taste horrible. But even if an animal escapes after it has been caught, it can still be hurt. So poisonous animals are often brightly colored. This warns predators not to even try to catch them.

   Some brightly colored frogs have toxic skin. Many poisonous frogs live in rain forests in South America. Unlike most frogs, these bright frogs are active during the day when their warning colors can be seen.

   The yellow poison frog shown on page 25 eats ants. The acid in the ants produces a strong poison in this frog's brightly colored skin.

1 Are these sentences True or False? Color in the star next to the correct answer.

(a) Poisonous animals often taste horrible and are brightly colored.

☆ True   ☆ False

(b) Poisonous frogs move about at night when their colors shine in the dark.

☆ True   ☆ False

(c) Yellow poison frogs are toxic because of the ants that they eat.

☆ True   ☆ False

2 Add letters to these words to make words that are in the story.

(a) p o i s o n ....

(b) w a r n ....

(c) b r i g h t ....

(d) a c t ....

3 Search the word puzzle for the words in the list below and circle them.

ACID
ACTIVE
ANTS
BRIGHTLY
FROGS
POISONOUS
PREDATORS
SKIN
TASTE
TOXIC
WARNS

P	R	E	D	A	T	O	R	S
A	B	R	I	G	H	T	L	Y
T	C	F	R	O	G	S	W	S
A	O	T	O	U	T	H	A	T
S	L	A	I	A	M	N	R	O
T	O	N	E	V	I	R	N	X
E	R	T	I	K	E	C	S	I
A	S	S	S	A	C	I	D	C
P	O	I	S	O	N	O	U	S

4 There are 12 letters that have not been circled. Use the leftover letters to make a mystery phrase:

....

Does the frog's skin look bright or dull?

Vanishing Forests

Learn about why we need our forests. Look at Panama in an atlas to see how big it is. Then have fun completing the activities.

Factories and motor vehicles send carbon into the air. Trees in forests soak up this carbon. But many forests are disappearing. People log forests for timber. They use the timber to make buildings, furniture, and paper. They also clear forests for farms.

Between 2000 and 2005, 18 million acres (7.3 million ha) of forests around the world were cut down. This area is the size of Panama in Central America.

When people cut down forests, more than trees are destroyed. The homes of animals as small as butterflies and as large as chimpanzees and gorillas are lost. Many kinds of animals may die out as a result.

1 Complete these sentences by choosing the correct words. Color in the star next to each correct answer.

(a) Trees in forests .... factories and motor vehicles.

☆ help soak up the carbon made by

☆ supply the materials used to build

(b) From 2000 to 2005, ... was cleared of forest.

☆ the part of Africa where gorillas live

☆ an area the size of Panama

(c) Animals of many kinds .... in the world's forests.

☆ have to make their homes

☆ are hunted by people for food

2 Color in the stars next to the words that rhyme with these words from the story.

(a) butterflies

☆ wise   ☆ size   ☆ burn   ☆ skies

(b) trees

☆ world   ☆ please   ☆ chimpanzees   ☆ breeze

(c) lost

☆ cost   ☆ leaf   ☆ tossed   ☆ crossed

(d) clear

☆ disappear   ☆ fair   ☆ here   ☆ year

3 Look at the picture then circle the words in the box that describe the scene.

butterflies	tall trees	green	bricks
leaves	bulldozer	fence	soil

4 Now write a short poem about our disappearing forests.

....

....

....

....

....

....

....

....

....

....

....

....

Open for Trade

Let's find out when trade between Japan and countries like the USA began. Check a map to see how far Japan is from the USA. Have fun completing the activities when you finish reading the story.

Until the 1800s, there was little trade between Japan and other countries. In 1854, four American warships sailed into Edo Bay, in Japan. This is now called Tokyo Bay. A year later, the United States and Japan signed a treaty. They agreed to trade. Ships from Britain and France also began to come to Japan.

Many Japanese people, including the Royal Family, began wearing clothes like those worn in Europe and America. For them, this was the modern way to dress.

Japanese arts and crafts were taken to other countries. Artists in Europe and America saw this art. They copied ideas from what they saw.

1 Read the questions, then color in the star next to each correct answer.

(a) When did American warships first visit Japan?

☆ American warships first visited Japan in 1845.

☆ American warships first came to Japan in 1854.

(b) What sort of treaty did Japan and the United States sign in 1855?

☆ They signed a trade treaty.

☆ They signed a peace treaty.

(c) Why did the Japanese begin to wear clothes like those worn by people in America and Europe?

☆ Japanese people wore these clothes as they did not cost as much.

☆ The Japanese wore these clothes because they regarded them as modern.

2 Draw a line from each word to its meaning.

treaty   the buying, selling, or swapping of goods

trade   among them

modern   an agreement between countries

including   from the present time, up-to-date

3 Use the letters of the word "MODERN" to fill in this sudoku. Each letter appears once in each line across and down, and once in each mini-grid.

E		O	R		N
M			D		
				D	
N	R	D		E	O
D			E	R	
	E			N	

How were the American ships powered?

Talking on the Telephone

Here is some information about early telephones.
Read the story. Try to sound out new words.
Then enjoy completing the activities.

In 1876, Alexander Graham Bell invented a machine called a telephone. It turned sounds into electrical signals. These signals went along a wire. They turned back into sounds at the other end. Using telephones, people could talk over long distances.

George Coy invented the first telephone exchange. It opened in 1878 in New Haven, Connecticut, USA. It could handle only two telephone calls at once. Telephone exchanges soon became larger.

Telephone operators were women who connected telephone lines. The operator asked what number the caller wanted to speak to. The caller told the operator the number. The operator then connected the caller's line to that number.

1 Answer these questions about the story.

(a) When did Alexander Graham Bell invent the telephone?

....

(b) How many telephone calls could be made at the same time using the first telephone exchange?

....

(c) What did telephone operators do?

....

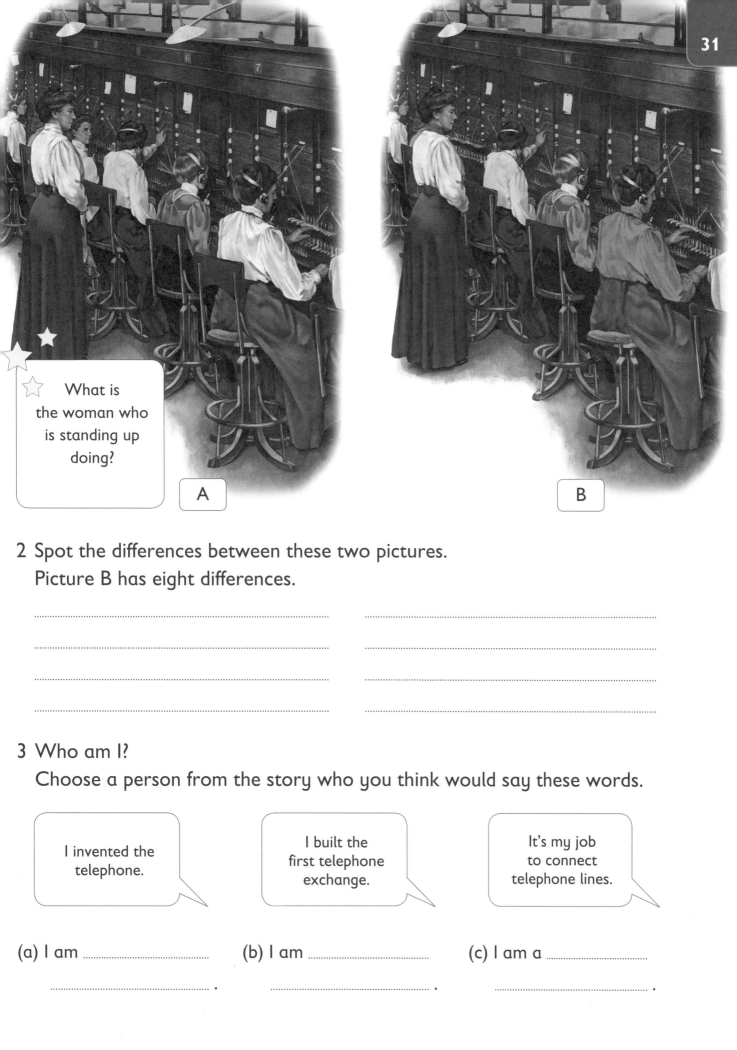

What is the woman who is standing up doing?

A

B

2 Spot the differences between these two pictures.
Picture B has eight differences.

....

....

....

....

3 Who am I?
Choose a person from the story who you think would say these words.

I invented the telephone.

I built the first telephone exchange.

It's my job to connect telephone lines.

(a) I am ....   (b) I am ....   (c) I am a ....

....

Built to Last

Earthquakes don't always knock buildings down. Find out why in this story. Then have fun completing the word activities.

Pagodas are temples that are shaped like pyramids. They are found throughout Asia. Some of these timber buildings have lasted for more than 1,000 years. Earthquakes have shaken them, but have not damaged them.

Earthquakes happen often in Japan. For a long time, Japanese people have tried to make buildings that can stand up to quakes. The temples in the picture are at Nara. They were built 1,300 years ago. At the center of each pagoda is a strong pole. The other parts are slotted together without nails. In an earthquake, they can move around without breaking apart.

1 Finish these sentences. Color in the star next to the correct answer.

(a) Pagodas are made from timber and they are ....

☆ shaped like pyramids.

☆ taller than skyscrapers.

☆ painted every year.

(b) Because Japan has always had lots of earthquakes, ...

☆ few tall buildings have ever been made there.

☆ the Japanese make buildings that can withstand them.

☆ all old Japanese buildings fell down long ago.

(c) The pagodas at Nara are made of a central pole ....

☆ with the other parts joined to it with long nails.

☆ and other wooden parts that are slotted together.

☆ which is set into concrete so it cannot move.

2 Which of these things is the odd one out? Color in the star next to the correct answer and then say why.

(a) ☆ pagoda   ☆ chair   ☆ skyscraper   ☆ pyramid

Why? ....

(b) ☆ jelly   ☆ timber   ☆ brick   ☆ concrete

Why? ....

(c) ☆ Japan   ☆ San Francisco   ☆ Asia   ☆ oak

Why? ....

3 Unscramble these letters to make words from the story.

(a) adgsoap   ....

(b) pemestl   ....

(c) terenc   ....

(d) stedla   ....

(e) keraginb   ....

A Big Family

Here is some information about elephant families. Have fun with the word puzzles and activities when you finish reading the story.

There are two types of elephants. One kind lives in Asia, and the other in Africa. African elephants are the largest animals that live on land.

Elephants live in family groups made up of adult females and their young. The adult females are mothers, daughters, sisters, and aunts of each other. An older female leads the group.

Elephants in a group care for each other and stay together. The elephants in the picture are cooling off in a waterhole. They suck water into their trunk and spray it on themselves.

When male elephants are close to becoming adults, they leave the group. They mostly live alone and visit groups only to breed.

1 Complete these sentences by choosing the correct words. Circle your answers.

   (a) No other ..animal / reptile.. that lives on land is as large as the
       ..Asian / African.. elephant.

   (b) Only adult ..males / females.. and their ..young / brothers.. live in
       elephant groups.

   (c) ..Adult / Elderly.. male elephants ..mostly / seldom.. live by themselves.

2 Here's a fun crossword. You will find clues to the answers in the story.

Across

5. A fully-grown animal. (5 letters)
8. The antonym of "smallest." (7)
9. The continent where the world's largest land animal lives. (6)
10. An animal with tusks and a trunk. (8)

Down

1. The continent where smaller elephants live. (4)
2. The female child of a mother or father. (8)
3. A group of animals that are related to each other. (6)
4. A pool of water in a dry place. (9)
6. A long pointed tooth on either side of the mouth of some animals. (4)
7. The sex that can give birth to babies or produce eggs. (6)

The First Americans

In this story, find out how people first reached the Americas. Look at an atlas or globe of the world to see where they crossed over from Asia. Complete the activities when you finish reading the story.

More than 15,000 years ago, the world was much colder than it is now. Much more water was frozen in glaciers and sea ice. This meant there was less water in the oceans. Sea levels were much lower.

At this time, there was land between Siberia, in Asia, and Alaska, in North America. It was like a great bridge. Herds of grazing animals went out onto this land bridge. The animals moved between Asia and North America.

People from Asia followed the herds. They hunted the animals with stone-tipped spears. These people became the earliest American Indians. Eventually, they spread out across the continent and into South America.

1 Are these sentences True or False? Color in the star next to the correct answer.

(a) Around 15,000 years ago, there was more water in the oceans than there is today.

☆ True   ☆ False

(b) Great herds of animals moved between Asia and America across a bridge of land.

☆ True   ☆ False

(c) The earliest people to live in America came from Australia.

☆ True   ☆ False

2 Number these sentences in the correct order.

.... Hunters follow the herds of animals.

.... Earth becomes colder.

.... People spread across North America and into South America.

.... People reach North America from Asia.

.... Water is frozen in glaciers and sea levels drop.

.... Herds of animals move out across new land.

3 Search the word puzzle for the words in the list below and
circle them.

AGO
ALASKA
AMERICA
EARLIEST
FROZEN
GLACIERS
HERDS
HUNTED
ICE
LEVEL
SEA
SIBERIA
SPEARS

E	A	R	L	I	E	S	T	L
F	H	U	N	T	E	D	A	N
R	E	S	I	B	E	R	I	A
O	R	D	B	R	I	A	G	O
Z	D	D	G	L	E	V	E	L
E	S	P	E	A	R	S	S	E
N	A	L	A	S	K	A	E	I
A	M	E	R	I	C	A	A	C
G	L	A	C	I	E	R	S	E

4 There are 10 letters that have not been circled.
Use the leftover letters to find the mystery phrase.

....

Rock Climbing

Find out about the special equipment rock climbers use. If you find a new word, look at the words around it to help work out the meaning. Try the word puzzles, too.

People of all ages enjoy the challenge of climbing on large rocks and up steep cliff faces. Rock climbers wear specially designed shoes and light clothing.

Climbers also wear harnesses, which are devices that are strapped around the body. Ropes attached to the harness are anchored to rocks. The harnesses and ropes keep climbers safe if they fall. Rock climbers often work in pairs. As one person climbs, another on the ground pulls on the rope to make sure it is not too loose.

People who climb on icy cliffs or glaciers use ice axes to cut holes in the ice where their feet can go.

1 Finish each sentence. Color in the star next to the correct answer.

(a) The harnesses that climbers wear are ....

☆ worn strapped around their body.

☆ made of rope woven with steel thread.

(b) When two climbers work together, one climbs while the other ....

☆ goes above to pull on the ropes.

☆ remains below and pulls on the rope.

(c) People who climb in icy places use ice axes to ....

☆ chop the ice from around their frozen ropes.

☆ to cut holes in the ice where they can put their feet.

2 Add letters to these words to make words that are in the story.

   (a) ..c.. ..l.. ..i.. ..m.. ..b.. ....

   (b) ..s.. ..p.. ..e.. ..c.. ..i.. ..a.. ..l.. ....

   (c) ..c.. ..l.. ..o.. ..t.. ..h.. ....

   (d) ..s.. ..t.. ..r.. ..a.. ..p.. ....

3 Use the letters of the word "CLIMBS" to fill in this sudoku. Each letter appears once in each line across and down, and once in each mini-grid.

M		L			
		I	L	S	
I	M		B		S
	L		C	M	
S					
L	C		S		

Do you know why this climber is wearing bright clothes?

Amazing Africa

Let's read about Africa. Look at an atlas to see what other countries are in this continent. Complete the fun activities when you finish reading the story.

There are 53 countries in Africa. People of many cultures live there. They have many different ways of doing things. The Masai people live in Kenya and Tanzania. The Masai man in the picture is doing a traditional dance.

The Sahara, the world's biggest desert, is in Africa's north. The Nile, the world's longest river, winds along the eastern side of Africa. It ends in Egypt. Across Africa's center is a thick band of rain forest. Africa also has vast grasslands. Many kinds of animals live there. Some feed on the grasses, while others eat the grass-eaters. People from around the world visit Africa to watch animals such as lions, zebras, and elephants.

1 Answer these questions about the story.
   Color in the star next to each correct answer.

   (a) Where is the largest desert in the world?

      ☆ The world's biggest desert runs along Africa's western side.

      ☆ The largest desert in the world is in the north of Africa.

   (b) Why do many people from around the world visit Africa?

      ☆ Many people visit Africa to see wild animals such as lions and elephants.

      ☆ Many people visit Africa to see emus and ostriches.

   (c) In what African countries do the Masai people live?

      ☆ They live in Tanzania and Kenya.

      ☆ The Masai people live in the Sahara.

2 Draw a line from each place in Africa to the clue that describes it.

Sahara   a country where the Masai live

Nile   the continent where wild zebras live

Kenya   the world's longest river

Egypt   the country where the Nile River ends

Africa   the world's biggest desert

3 Take letters away from these words to make words that are in the story.

(a) watchful   ....

(b) riverbed   ....

(c) uneaten   ....

(d) always   ....

(e) rewinds   ....

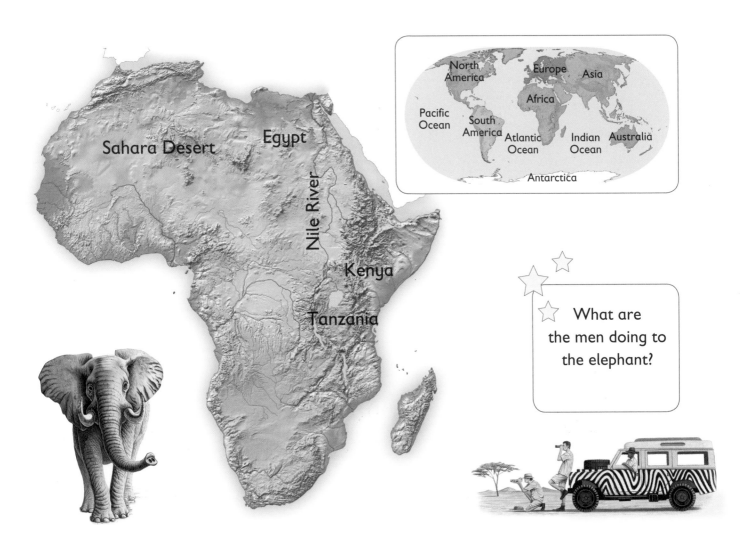

What are the men doing to the elephant?

Honey-makers

Where do we get honey? From bees. Look closely at the picture on page 43 to spot the different bees that are mentioned in the story. Then complete the fun activities.

Many bees live in large groups in nests, or hives. In a bee colony, the queen bee lays all the eggs. Male bees, called drones, mate with the queen. Female worker bees gather food, care for the young insects, called larvae, and look after the nest.

Nectar is a sweet liquid made by flowers. Worker bees gather it to make into honey for food. Flowers also make pollen, a substance like dust. Bees gather pollen to eat. As a bee goes from flower to flower, some pollen brushes onto and off its hairy body. When pollen from flowers of the same kind mixes, the flowers can produce seeds.

1 Complete these sentences by choosing the correct words.
Circle your answers.

(a) In a bee ..colony / class.. the worker bees look after the ..larvae / king...

(b) Bees ..collect / wash.. the nectar from ..fruit / flowers.. to make into honey.

(c) Each beehive has only one ..drone / queen.., and she produces all of the ..honey / eggs...

2 Who am I?

Look at the picture and read the story to help work out which bee you think would say these words.

> The worker bee is feeding me honey.

> I am the biggest bee. I lay one egg in each chamber.

> I am returning to the hive with pollen and nectar.

(a) I am a ....   (b) I am the ....   (c) I am a ....

3 Draw a line between the word from the story and its meaning.

larvae	a sweet fluid made by flowers
gather	a male bee
produce	collect
nectar	young insects
drone	make something

4 Spot the differences between these two pictures. Picture B has eight differences.

....

....

....

....

> How do bees carry the yellow pollen they have collected?

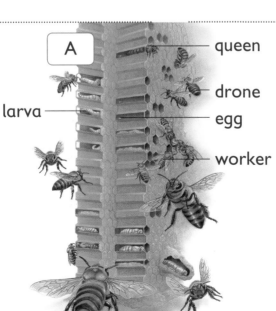

A

larva

queen
drone
egg
worker

B

Sailing West

Read about Christopher Columbus's voyages. If you come to a word you do not know, look at the words around it to help work out its meaning.

In 1492, Christopher Columbus set sail from Spain. He commanded a fleet of three ships. They sailed west across the Atlantic Ocean. After two months at sea, there was great excitement when a sailor saw land. The fleet of ships had reached islands in the Caribbean Sea. Columbus thought they were in Asia and named these islands the West Indies.

The *Santa Maria* was the ship in which Columbus sailed from Spain. It was wrecked among the islands of the Caribbean.

In 1498, Columbus reached mainland South America on his third voyage west. His ships explored the Orinoco River in the country that is now called Venezuela.

1 Answer these questions about the story.

(a) What was the name of the ship in Columbus's fleet that was wrecked?

....

(b) Why did Columbus name the islands in the Caribbean the West Indies?

....

(c) How long did Columbus's first voyage across the Atlantic Ocean take?

....

2 Number these sentences in the correct order.

.... A sailor sights land.

.... Two ships return to Spain.

.... The *Santa Maria* is wrecked.

.... Columbus's fleet sets sail from Spain.

.... Columbus names the West Indies.

.... The fleet sails from Spain across the Atlantic Ocean.

3 Can you help the *Santa Maria* find her way through the maze to get to land?

land

A Telescope in Space

Here is information about the Hubble Space Telescope. Read the story and look closely at the picture to help you complete the activities.

The Hubble Space Telescope was named after the scientist Edwin Hubble. It was sent into orbit around Earth in 1990. It collects signals given off by stars, planets, and other objects in space. These signals are sent to Earth, where they are turned into pictures.

This space telescope provides the clearest pictures of space ever taken. It has helped make many important discoveries. For example, in 1995, the telescope was used to create a photo of clouds of gas far away from Earth in space, where stars can form. These clouds are called the Pillars of Creation.

The telescope goes around Earth every 90 minutes. Sometimes astronauts fly out into space to repair it.

1 Are these sentences True or False? Color in the star next to the correct answer.

(a) The Hubble Space Telescope collects signals sent by spaceships.

☆ True   ☆ False

(b) The Pillars of Creation are clouds of gas in Earth's atmosphere.

☆ True   ☆ False

(c) Signals sent to Earth from the Hubble Space Telescope are made into pictures.

☆ True   ☆ False

2 A word that means the same as another word is called a synonym.
Choose a synonym for each of these words. Circle the correct answer.

(a) orbit

> go over   go around   go under

(b) turned

> changed   used   pointed

(c) objects

> foolish   fixes   things

(d) called

> sang   named   photographed

4 Find the letters A, B, C, and D in the picture. Write one letter next to each label below to show where that label should go in the picture.

.... light entering telescope

.... antenna

.... telescope door

.... solar panel

Wandering Wildebeest

Read this story about the journey of the wildebeest. When you come to a difficult word, break it into smaller parts to help you sound it out.

Wildebeest are hoofed animals that graze on grass. Each year, huge numbers of wildebeest travel across part of southern Africa. In May, the rainy season ends. Then the wildebeest move from Tanzania north to Kenya. Water and grass can still be found there. In November, the rain returns. The wildebeest begin the journey south to feed on fresh grass.

During the migration, the wildebeest must cross rivers such as the Mara River in Kenya. The wildebeest come together at good crossing places. This is the most dangerous part of the journey. Crocodiles attack as the swimming wildebeest. Some wildebeest also drown or are trampled.

1 Complete these sentences. Color in the star next to the correct answer.

(a) Wildebeest travel .... when the dry season begins.

☆ to the mountains in South Africa

☆ north from Tanzania to Kenya

(b) Sometimes wildebeest .... as they cross the Mara River.

☆ are attacked by crocodiles

☆ hold on to each other's tail

(c) The wildebeest migrate .... because of the seasons.

☆ in part of southern Africa

☆ across the north of Africa

2 Add letters to these words to make words that are in the story.

(a) .w.. ..i.. ..l.. ..d.. ....

(b) ..c.. ..r.. ..o.. ..s.. ..s.. ....

(c) ..t.. ..r.. ..a.. ..m.. ..p.. ....

(d) ..d.. ..a.. ..n.. ..g.. ..e.. ..r.. ....

(e) ..h.. ..o.. ..o.. ..f.. ....

3 Here's a fun crossword. The answers are words in the story.

Across
1. Trodden on heavily. (8 letters)
4. Having hoofs. (6)
5. Large reptiles that live in rivers and
   eat other animals. (10)
9. A country in southern Africa. (5)
10. The second-last month of the year. (8)

Down
2. One of the seven continents. (6)
3. A part of the year with a certain kind
   of weather. (6)
6. Having a lot of rain. (5)
7. To die when you are underwater and
   cannot breathe. (5)
8. To eat grass. (5)

Fossil Fuels

What do you know about fossil fuels? As you read the story, underline any new words you come across. Can you work out what they mean?

The electricity we use in our homes and cities comes mainly from burning coal. We rely on oil to run our vehicles. We use gas for cooking and heating. Coal, oil, and gas come from inside Earth and were formed over thousands of years. They are called fossil fuels.

For centuries, people mined coal underground by hand. Today, miners operate machines that do most of the work. Machines can mine a lot of coal quickly. People drill for oil and gas beneath Earth's surface.

As we use more and more oil, gas, and coal, the amount that remains in Earth gets smaller and smaller. One day these fossil fuels will all be used up.

1 Complete these sentences by choosing the correct words. Circle your answers.

(a) We use gas for ..cooling / cooking.. and ..heating / eating...

(b) Once people ..mined / planted.. coal by hand but ..now / never.. they use machines.

(c) One day the ..fossil / frozen.. fuels that we ..rent / use.. will all be used up.

(d) We rely on ..coal / oil.. to run our ..vehicles / computers...

(e) Coal, ..soil / oil.., and gas come from ..inside / near. Earth.

2 Draw a line between the sentences that mean the same thing.

People once mined coal by hand.   Coal is a fuel used to make electricity.

One day, fossil fuels will run out.   People drill for gas and oil beneath Earth's surface.

Electricity is made by burning coal.   We are using up Earth's gas, oil, and coal.

Gas and oil are reached under Earth's surface by drilling.   In the past, people mined coal without machines.

3 Find the letters A, B, C, and D in the picture. Write one letter next to each label below to show where that label should go in the picture.

.... Coal is taken up to the surface.

.... trucks that are filled with coal

.... Miners go down into the mine.

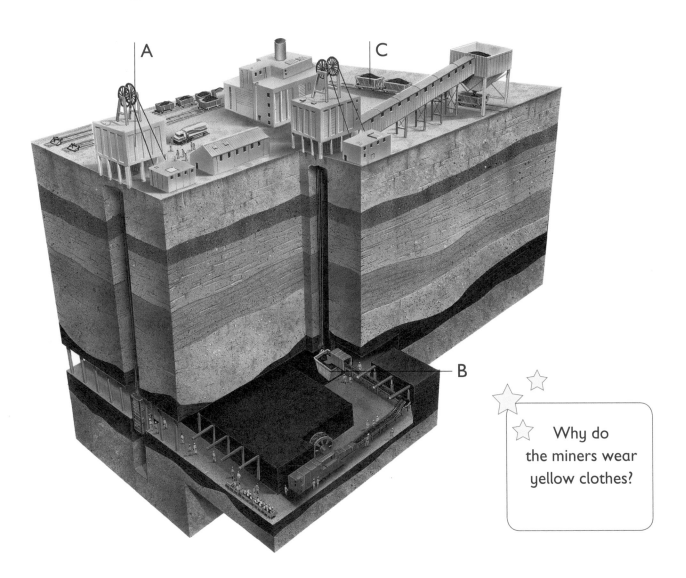

Why do the miners wear yellow clothes?

Computer Communication

So just what is the Internet? Read this story and find out, and then complete the fun word activities.

The Internet is a communication system that can send vast amounts of information around the world in moments. It has been created by connecting networks of computers to each other.

Using the Internet, people can send sounds, writing, photographs, and even films. The Internet sends information as electronic signals. The signals are sent using telephone lines, cell phone equipment, or satellites.

The early computers of the 1940s were large. They filled whole rooms. Today's computers are small enough to fit on a desk. They are called desktop computers. Now, even tiny cell phones can receive information using the Internet.

1 These are questions about the story. Color in the stars next the correct answers.

(a) How large were computers made in the 1940s?

☆ Computers of the 1940s were as large as a car.

☆ They were much smaller than today's computers.

☆ They were so large that they filled whole rooms.

(b) How fast can the Internet send information around the world?

☆ It can send information around the world in moments.

☆ The Internet can send information in just a matter of hours.

☆ It can send information at three times the speed of light.

(c) How do computers send information to each other?

☆ Computers send information to each other as sound signals.

☆ They send each other information as electronic signals.

☆ Computers send out information as satellite signals.

2 Have a look at page 9 for an example of a word ladder.
   Now it's your turn.

   Change the word "send" into the word "vast."
   Fill the table with the words.

s	e	n	d
v	a	s	t

3 Use the clues below to find these words in the story.

   (a) This word is a verb (a doing word). It rhymes with "mend." It means to
       make something go somewhere.

       The word is: ....d... .

   (b) This word is a noun (the name of a thing). It rhymes with "shooter."
       It is a machine that works using electronic signals.

       The word is: ....t... ....

   (c) This word is a noun (the name of a thing). It rhymes with "cent."
       It is something you need to do a job.

       The word is: ....p... ....n... ....

Studying Volcanoes

Who or what is a volcanologist? Find out in this story.
Use a dictionary to find out the meanings of new words.

People who study volcanoes are called volcanologists. They use
aircraft and space satellites to record eruptions and their effects.
They also climb up and into volcanoes. There, they collect samples
of lava and take measurements. It is often dangerous work.

Volcanologists work in teams. They all have different jobs. Some
use an instrument to measure the temperature of lava. They wear
special clothing that protects them from the great heat. Others
study the gases that come out of volcanoes. They wear gas masks.
Volcanologists also measure the size of craters, and movements in
the ground caused by volcanic activity.

1 Answer these questions about the story.

    (a) Why do volcanologists go up and into volcanoes?

    ....

    (b) How do volcanologists get close enough to lava to measure
        its temperature?

    ....

    (c) Why do volcanologists study volcanoes?

    ....

    (d) Why do some volcanologists wear gas masks?

    ....

2 Use these clues to find smaller words made by letters in the word "volcanologist."

(a) A space between two posts where players kick a ball.

   ...g.. ....

(b) A seat with no arms or back for one person.

   ....l..

(c) A mountain formed by gas and magma pushing upward from beneath Earth's surface.

   ....o...

(d) Not knowing which way you should go.

   ....s... ....

(e) Something used to do work.

   ....l..

3 Spot the differences between these two pictures. Picture B has seven differences.

....

....

....

....

....

....

....

A

B

Aztec Warriors

Let's read this story about Aztec warriors. When you come to a difficult word, break it into smaller parts to help you sound it out.

Aztecs were warlike people. All young Aztec men trained as soldiers. They waged wars in order to take prisoners. The captives were killed as human sacrifices to the Aztec gods. These sacrifices were carried out in religious ceremonies at temples.

The Aztecs believed that different gods and goddesses looked after separate things. They thought that their sun god would not move across the sky if they didn't make human sacrifices to him. They made sacrifices of children to their rain god so he would bring rain to water their crops.

Warriors who took many prisoners were respected. They were allowed to wear elaborate uniforms.

1 Are these sentences True or False? Color in the star next to the correct answer.

(a) The Aztecs sacrificed their prisoners to their gods and goddesses.

☆ True   ☆ False

(b) Each Aztec family sent one son to train as a soldier.

☆ True   ☆ False

(c) Aztec warriors wore elaborate costumes to please their prisoners.

☆ True   ☆ False

2 A word that means the same as another word is called a synonym.
Draw lines between the synonyms in each column.

warriors	person
prisoners	valued
human	soldiers
move	captives
respected	travel

3 Search the word puzzle for the words in the list below
and circle them.

AZTEC
CAPTIVES
CROPS
GODS
RAIN
SKY
TEMPLES
UNIFORMS
WAGED
WARLIKE
WARRIORS
WARS

C	U	N	I	F	O	R	M	S
A	H	U	W	A	R	S	T	W
P	Z	W	A	G	E	D	E	A
T	C	T	M	A	N	G	M	R
I	R	S	E	A	C	O	P	R
V	O	R	I	C	F	D	L	I
E	P	I	C	E	S	S	E	O
S	S	R	A	I	N	K	S	R
W	A	R	L	I	K	E	Y	S

4 There are 14 letters that have not been circled. Use the leftover letters
to make this mystery phrase:

……… ……… ……… ……… ……… ……… ……… ……… ……… ……… ……… ……… ……… ………

Terrible Talons

Here is some information about animals with talons. Read the story and then enjoy completing the fun activities.

Claws are important weapons for many predators. Animals such as lions and polar bears use their claws to grab and hold their prey. Birds of prey, such as eagles, ospreys, and owls, also use claws, called talons, when they hunt.

Talons are long and curved like hooks. Different kinds of birds of prey have feet and talons of different shapes and sizes. Each bird's feet suit the animals it hunts.

Ospreys live near seas, rivers, and lakes. They plunge feet first into the water and grab fish in their talons. The rough, spiky flesh on the underside of an osprey's toes helps it keep a firm grip on slippery fish.

1 Finish these sentences. Color in the star next to the correct answer.

(a) Many predators, such as polar bears, use claws mainly

☆ to groom their long fur to stay clean and healthy.

☆ as weapons to catch the animals that they eat.

☆ to bury the animals that they catch to eat later.

(b) Birds of prey have claws called talons that are

☆ so sharp they can pierce a turtle's shell.

☆ rough and spiky, like a shark's teeth.

☆ long and curved, just like hooks.

(c) Ospreys are a kind of bird of prey that lives

☆ on other birds it catches in the air.

☆ in the desert and hunts at night.

☆ close to seas, lakes, and rivers.

2 A word that sounds the same as another word is called a homophone.
Circle the correct word in each sentence.

   (a) Birds of ..pray../..prey.. have sharp talons.

   (b) Polar bears catch seals with ..their../..there.. claws.

   (c) The fish have slippery skin, not ..ruff../..rough.. skin.

3 Have a look at page **9** for an example of a word ladder.
Now it's your turn.

Change the word "prey" into the word "claw."
Fill the table with the words.

p	r	e	y
c	l	a	w

Powered by the Sun

Read about solar energy in this story. If you come to a word you don't know, look at the words around it to help work out its meaning.

The Sun sends huge amounts of energy to Earth. This solar energy can be used to heat things, or to make electricity—without making pollution. The Sun will still be shining long after the last coal and oil have been mined.

The rows of solar panels on the roof of the house in the picture turn the Sun's energy into electricity. This energy can be stored in batteries. It can also travel along power lines into the electricity system.

Solar water heaters absorb the Sun's energy to heat water. This hot water is stored in a tank, which can be seen above the two heating panels.

1 Complete each sentence by choosing the correct words. Circle your answers.

(a) Energy from the ..solar../.Sun.. can make electricity ..without./.into.. making pollution.

(b) Solar ..platforms./.panels.. are often placed on the ..walls./.roof.. of a house to collect energy.

(c) Hot ..water./.weather.. made by a solar water heater is ..stored./.steamed.. in a tank for use.

2 Choose the words that rhyme with these words from the story.
  Color in the stars next to the correct answers.

(a) panels

☆ pants   ☆ channels   ☆ howls

(b) solar

☆ polar   ☆ roller   ☆ start

(c) coal

☆ bowl   ☆ hole   ☆ foal

(d) Earth

☆ ear   ☆ birth   ☆ worth

water tank

solar panel

3 Match the jigsaw parts to make sentences. Use different colors to match
  the sentence parts.

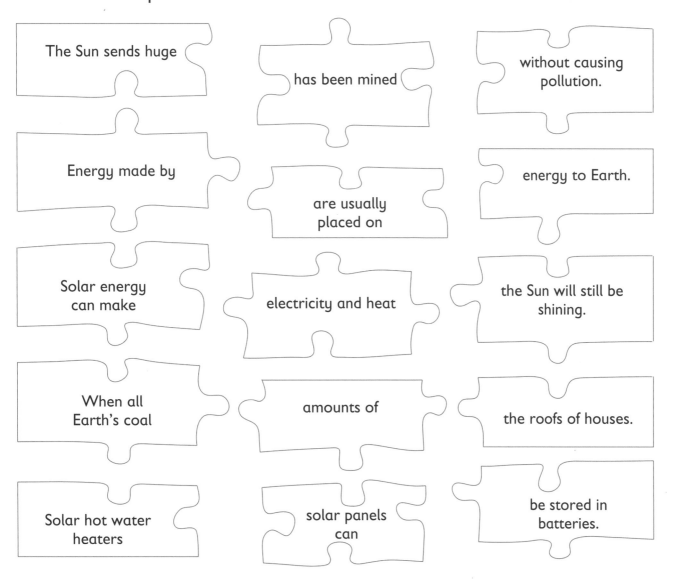

The Sun sends huge

has been mined

without causing pollution.

Energy made by

are usually placed on

energy to Earth.

Solar energy can make

electricity and heat

the Sun will still be shining.

When all Earth's coal

amounts of

the roofs of houses.

Solar hot water heaters

solar panels can

be stored in batteries.

Silk Road

Read about the famous traveler Marco Polo. Look at the map to see where he went and what he saw on his journeys. Then have fun completing the activities.

In 1272, young Marco Polo set out from Venice in Italy with his father and uncle. For three years they traveled, by sea and over land, to China. They followed a route that we now call the Silk Road. Centuries earlier, Chinese traders had first carried silk and other goods along this route.

Marco Polo returned to Venice in 1295. He wrote a book about his journeys. He wrote about riding camels across the harsh Gobi Desert. He also wrote about working for the Mongol Emperor, Kublai Khan.

Through Marco Polo's book, Europeans became more interested in Asia. Other explorers and traders went there.

1 Look at the picture and read the story to answer these questions.

(a) Who did Marco Polo work for when he was north of China in Mongolia?

....

(b) What animals did Marco Polo see at the southermost point of his journey through China?

....

(c) How many years was Marco Polo away from Venice?

....

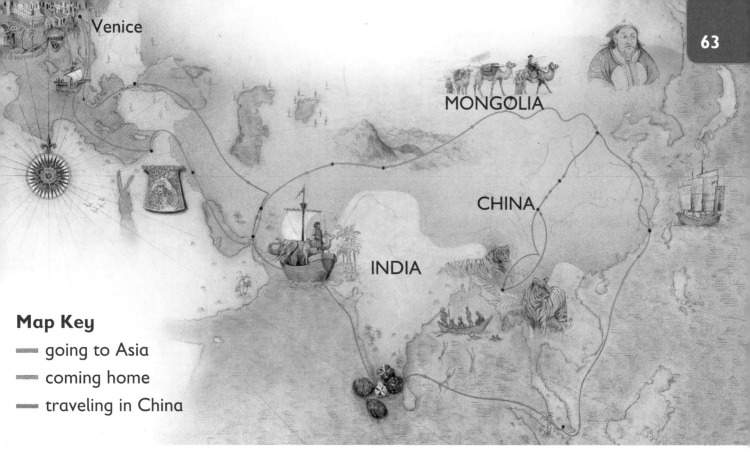

Venice

MONGOLIA

CHINA

INDIA

Map Key

— going to Asia

— coming home

— traveling in China

2 Who am I?

Choose a person from the word box who you think would say these words.

| Marco Polo   explorer   camel   Kublai Khan   captain   elephant |

> After I read Marco Polo's book, I had to see Asia.

> I traveled from Venice to China and back again.

> Marco Polo worked for me.

(a) I am an ....   (b) I am ....   (c) I am ....

3 Use the letters of the word "TRAVEL" to fill in this sudoku. Each letter appears once in each line across and down, and once in each mini-grid.

	L		E		
A				R	
L	E		A		R
				L	
	A		T	V	
	T			E	A

Earthquake Rescuers

Read the story about rescue workers. If you come across a word you don't know, look it up in a dictionary. Complete the fun activities when you finish reading the story.

When the ground stops shaking after an earthquake, rescue workers are quick to arrive. Sirens sound and helicopters hover overhead. Rescuers search buildings and dig through the rubble. They listen everywhere for sounds of life. They must work quickly to find trapped survivors on or buried under the ground.

Earthquakes often destroy roads. Helicopters provide the only means of carrying injured survivors to hospital.

Rescuers have a difficult and dangerous job. Cut power lines can cause fires and broken gas pipes can release deadly fumes. The mixture of gas and fires often causes sudden explosions.

1 Are these sentences True or False? Color in the star next to the correct answer.

(a) Rescue workers always work slowly so they don't trigger more earthquakes.

☆ True   ☆ False

(b) After an earthquake, there are often explosions caused when gas and fire mix together.

☆ True   ☆ False

(c) Helicopters are never used in rescue work because rescuers need quiet to hear buried survivors.

☆ True   ☆ False

2 Imagine you are a reporter watching the scene in the picture. Write a short news bulletin describing the dangers the rescue workers face.

....

....

....

....

....

....

....

....

....

....

....

3 Draw a line from the word to its meaning.

rescue	gas or smoke that can be seen or smelled
injured	a person who is still alive after a disaster
rubble	harmed or hurt
fumes	broken pieces of brick, stone or concrete
survivor	save from danger or harm

4 Look at the picture then circle the words that describe the scene.

smashed	lava	glass	burning
crane	rubble	peaceful	concrete

Giant of the Ocean

Read this story about blue whales. If you find a new word, look at the words around it to help work out the meaning.

The biggest animal in the world lives in the sea. It is the blue whale. This largest of all creatures feeds on some of the very smallest of sea animals. They are called krill, and they look like tiny shrimps.

When it is born, a blue whale calf is about 23 feet (7 m) long. Blue whales can grow up to about 98 feet (30 m) long. Female blue whales always grow larger than males. An adult female blue whale weighs 26 times as much as an elephant. Its huge heart is the same size as a small car.

1 These are questions about the story. Color in the stars next the correct answers.

(a) How long is a blue whale calf when it is born?

☆ A blue whale calf is as long as 26 small cars when it is born.

☆ When it is born, a blue whale is about 23 feet (7 m) long.

☆ When a blue whale is born it is 98 feet (30 m) in length.

(b) How big is a fully grown female blue whale's heart?

☆ A female blue whale's heart is as big as an elephant.

☆ Its heart is as large as a newborn blue whale calf.

☆ It has a heart about the same size as a small car.

(c) What does the largest creature in the world eat?

☆ Blue whales eat tiny shrimp-like creatures called krill.

☆ Elephants eat huge amounts of leaves every day.

☆ Krill feast on the dead bodies of blue whales.

2 Which of these things is the odd one out? Why?

(a) ☆ elephant　　☆ car　　☆ tree　　☆ whale

Why? ....

(b) ☆ calf　　☆ caterpillar　　☆ duckling　　☆ bee

Why? ....

(c) ☆ elephant　　☆ squid　　☆ shrimp　　☆ whale

Why? ....

(d) ☆ car　　☆ drill　　☆ whale　　☆ telephone

Why? ....

3 Use the letters of the word "WEIGHS" to fill in this sudoku. Each letter appears once in each line across and down, and once in each mini-grid.

		I			
				E	
	W	H	E		G
W			I		H
	G	W			S
			G		

Answers

Crossword, sudoku, and other puzzle solutions are on page 71.

4–5

1 (a) True (b) False (c) True

2 (a) poorer person (b) rich woman (c) artist

3 (a) picture. Because it is the only one that is not a kind of material.

(b) houses. Because they are the only things not made from silk.

(c) fish. Because it is an animal, and the others are kinds of cloth.

(d) bowl. Because the others are all things that you wear.

Star box: bird, dragon, butterfly

6–7

1 (a) lava, hot ash, and gases (b) from its crater

(c) through cracks in Earth's surface

2 magma — a mountain pushed up from Earth's surface by magma and gas

lava — a wide, bowl-shaped opening at the top of a volcano

volcano — magma that has come out of a volcano

crater — hot, melted rock

3 Word search

4 volcanic eruption

Star box: red

8–9

1 (a) protect the wings they use to fly.

(b) in pieces of animal dung. (c) bury the balls under the ground.

2 Word ladder

3 Maze

10–11

1 (a) cook, warm (b) bake, metal (c) hotter, blowing

2 (a) clay (b) fire (c) soil (d) pots

3 When things burn they give off energy as light and heat.

The first metal objects were made about 8,000 years ago.

Metal is made by heating soil and rock that contain metal elements.

Fire was first used to cook food and to give light and warmth.

Ancient Egyptians blew through clay-tipped reeds to make fires hotter.

Star box: to stop the reeds from catching fire

12–13

1 (a) They lay their eggs on the ground in shallow hollows.

(b) They fly to near the South Pole, where it is summer.

(c) They eat fish that they catch in the ocean.

2 (a) ends (b) hollow (c) thin

3 Crossword

14–15

1 (a) on public roads (b) 1903 (c) July

2 The Tour de France is held over three weeks — The cyclist who is winning wears a yellow jersey.

The Tour de France is held on public roads. — It takes 21 days to complete the Tour de France.

The yellow jersey is worn by the rider coming first in the race. — Cars normally travel on roads where the Tour de France is run.

3 yellow jersey, mountains, flags, crowds, motorcycle, cyclists

Star box: to protect their head

16–17

1 (a) False (b) False (c) True

2 (a) Submersibles can go very deep into the deep ocean.

(b) Scientists collect samples using submersibles.

(c) Robots control some submersibles.

3 Crossword

Star box: No

18–19

1 (a) about one-third (b) seven (c) because Earth's surface is made up of tectonic plates that move

2 Asia is the biggest continent. 3 Sudoku

Star box: Antarctica

20–21

1 (a) They used feathers to make magnificent headdresses.

(b) Masks were often put over the faces of important people when they were buried.

(c) They were used to grind chilies and other plant foods.

2 (a) dull (b) unimportant (c) destroy (d) lived

3
mask — clay
cloak — gold
statue — feathers
pot — stone

22–23

1 (a) stars, constellations (b) thought, gods

(c) movements, charts

2 (a) Leo the lion (b) Gemini the twins (c) Cancer the crab

3 (a) nation (b) station (c) cents (d) late (e) notion (f) cast

Star box: no, only some

24–25

1 (a) True (b) False (c) True

2 (a) poisonous (b) warning (c) brightly (d) active

3 Word search

4 South America

Star box: bright

26–27

1 (a) help soak up the carbon made by

(b) an area the size of Panama (c) have to make their homes

2 (a) wise, size, skies (b) please, chimpanzees, breeze

(c) cost, tossed, crossed (d) disappear, here, year

3 butterflies, tall trees, green, leaves, bulldozer, soil

28–29

1 (a) American warships first came to Japan in 1854.

(b) They signed a trade treaty.

(c) The Japanese wore these clothes because they regarded them as modern.

2 treaty — an agreement between countries
trade — the buying, selling, or swapping of goods
modern — from the present time, up-to-date
including — among them

3 Sudoku

Star box: by sail and by steam

30–31

1 (a) 1876   (b) two   (c) connected telephone lines

2 collar of standing woman's shirt a different color

belt missing from standing woman

shirt of first seated woman on right a different color

first overhead light from right missing

extra metal band on headset of second seated woman on the right

number plate above the first seated woman on right missing

fourth seated woman on the right missing

back of one of the chairs missing

3 (a) Alexander Graham Bell   (b) George Coy

(c) a telephone operator

Star box: supervising the telephone operators

32–33

1 (a) shaped like pyramids

(b) the Japanese make buildings that can withstand them.

(c) and other wooden parts that are slotted together.

2 (a) chair. Because it is a type of furniture.

(b) jelly. Because it is a type of food.

(c) oak. Because it is a type of tree.

3 (a) pagodas   (b) temples   (c) center

(d) lasted   (e) breaking

34–35

1 (a) animal, African   (b) females, young   (c) Adult, mostly

3 Crossword

Star box: six

36–37

1 (a) False   (b) True   (c) False

2 4 Hunters follow the herds of animals.

1 Earth becomes colder.

6 People spread across North America and into South America.

5 People reach North America from Asia.

2 Water is frozen in glaciers and sea levels drop.

3 Herds of animals move out across new land.

3 Word search

4 land bridge

38–39

1 (a) worn strapped around their body.

(b) remains below and pulls on the rope.

(c) to cut holes in the ice where they can put their feet.

2 (a) climbers   (b) specially   (b) clothing   (c) strapped

3 Sudoku

Star box: so it is easy for the other climbers to see him

40–41

1 (a) The largest desert in the world is in the north of Africa.

(b) Many people visit Africa to see wild animals such as lions and elephants.

(c) They live in Tanzania and Kenya.

2 Sahara — the world's biggest desert
Nile — the world's longest river
Kenya — a country where the Masai live
Egypt — the country where the Nile River ends
Africa — the continent where wild zebras live

3 (a) watch   (b) river   (c) eat   (d) ways   (e) winds

Star box: watching with binoculars, taking photos

42–43

1 (a) colony, larvae

(b) collect, flowers

(c) queen, eggs

2 (a) larva

(b) queen bee

(c) worker bee

3 larvae — young insects
gather — collect
produce — make something
nectar — a sweet fluid made by flowers
drone — a male bee

44–45

1 (a) the *Santa Maria*

(b) because he thought they were in Asia

(c) two months

2 3 A sailor sights land.

6 Two ships return to Spain.

5 The Santa Maria is wrecked.

1 Columbus's fleet sets sail from Spain.

4 Columbus names the West Indies.

2 The fleet sails from Spain across the Atlantic Ocean.

3 Maze

Answers continued

46–47

1 (a) False   (b) False   (c) True

2 (a) go around   (b) changed   (c) things   (d) named

3 B light entering telescope
  D antenna
  A telescope door
  C solar panel

48–49

1 (a) north from Tanzania to Kenya
  (b) are attacked by crocodiles
  (c) in part of southern Africa

2 (a) wildebeest   (b) crossing   (c) trampled
  (d) dangerous   (e) hoofed

3 Crossword

50–51

1 (a) cooking, heating   (b) mined, now   (c) fossil, use
  (d) oil, vehicles   (e) oil, inside

2 People once mined coal by hand. — In the past, people mined coal without machines.
  One day, fossil fuels will run out. — We are using up Earth's gas, oil and coal.
  Electricity is made by burning coal. — Coal is a fuel used to make electricity.
  Gas and oil are reached under Earth's surface by drilling. — People drill for gas and oil beneath Earth's surface.

3 B Coal is taken up to the surface.
  C trucks that are filled with coal
  A Miners go down into the mine.

Star box: so they can see each other easily

52–53

1 (a) They were so large that they filled whole rooms.
  (b) It can send information around the world in moments.
  (c) They send each other information as electronic signals.

2 Word ladder

3 (a) send   (b) computer   (c) equipment

54–55

1 (a) to take measurements and collect lava samples
  (b) by wearing special clothing that protects them from the heat
  (c) to learn about volcanic eruptions and their effects
  (d) to protect themselves from the gases that come out of volcanoes

2 (a) goal   (b) stool   (c) volcano   (d) lost   (e) tool

3 extra scientific instrument next to man on left
  half of scientific instrument to his right missing
  extra spray of lava between him and other man in hard hat
  hard hat of second man from left changed color
  extra lava flow from him to the two men standing together
  scientific instruments on ground beside these two men missing
  man on top right missing

56–57

1 (a) True   (b) False   (c) False

2 warriors — soldiers
  prisoners — captives
  human — person
  move — travel
  respected — valued

3 Word search

4 human sacrifice

58–59

1 (a) as weapons to catch the animals that they eat.
  (b) long and curved, just like hooks.
  (c) close to seas, lakes, and rivers.

2 (a) prey   (b) their   (c) rough

3 Word ladder

60–61

1 (a) Sun, without   (b) panels, roof   (c) water, stored

2 (a) channels   (b) polar, roller   (c) bowl, hole, foal
  (d) birth, worth

3 The Sun sends huge amounts of energy to Earth.
  Energy made by solar panels can be stored in batteries.
  Solar energy can make electricity and heat without causing pollution.
  When all Earth's coal has been mined the Sun will still be shining.
  Solar hot water heaters are usually placed on the roofs of houses.

62–63

1 (a) Kublai Khan   (b) tigers   (c) 23 years

2 (a) explorer   (b) Marco Polo   (c) Kublai Khan

3 Sudoku

64–65

1 (a) False   (b) True   (c) False

3 rescue — save from danger or harm
  injured — harmed or hurt
  rubble — broken pieces of brick, stone or concrete
  fumes — gas or smoke that can be seen or smelled
  survivor — a person who is still alive after a disaster

4 smashed, glass, burning, crane, rubble, concrete

66–67

1 (a) When it is born, a blue whale is about 23 feet (7 m) long.
  (b) It has a heart about the same size as a small car.
  (c) Blue whales eat tiny shrimp-like creatures called krill.

2 (a) car. Because the others are all alive.
  (b) bee. Because the others are all young animals .
  (c) elephant. Because it is the only animal that lives on the land.
  (d) whale. Because it is an animal.

3 Sudoku

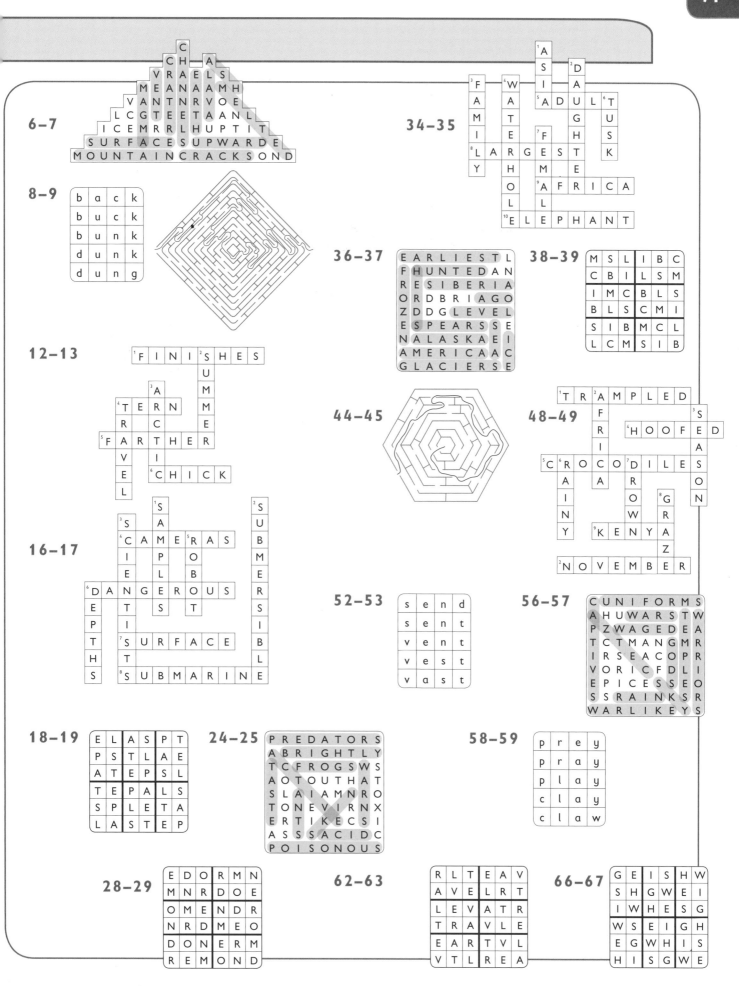

6–7

```
        C
      H A
  CHANNELS
  VRAEL S
MEANARAMHE
VANTNTRVOEL
LCGTEELTAANL
ICEMRRLHUPTIT
SURFACESUPWARDE
MOUNTAINCRACKSOND
```

8–9

b	a	c	k
b	u	c	k
b	u	n	k
d	u	n	k
d	u	n	g

12–13

1 FINISHES
2 SUMMER
3 ACTIVE
4 TERN
5 FARTHER
6 CHICK
(TRAVEL)

16–17

1 SA
2 SUBMERSIBLE
3 S
4 CAMERAS
5 ROBOT
6 DANGEROUS
7 SURFACE
8 SUBMARINE
(DEPTHS, SCIENTIST)

18–19

E	L	A	S	P	T
P	S	T	L	A	E
A	T	E	P	S	L
T	E	P	A	L	S
S	P	L	E	T	A
L	A	S	T	E	P

24–25

```
PREDATORS
ABRIGHTLY
TCFROGSWS
AOTOUTHAT
SLAIAMNRO
TONEVIRNX
ERTIKECSI
ASSSACIDC
POISONOUS
```

28–29

E	D	O	R	M	N
M	N	R	D	O	E
O	M	E	N	D	R
N	R	D	M	E	O
D	O	N	E	R	M
R	E	M	O	N	D

34–35

1 ASIA
2 DAUGHTER
3 FAMILY
4 WATERHOLE
5 ADULT
6 TUSK
7 FEMALE
8 LARGEST
9 AFRICA
10 ELEPHANT

36–37

```
EARLIESTL
FHUNTEDAN
RESIBERIA
ORDBRIAGO
ZDDGLEVEL
ESPEARSSE
NALASKAEI
AMERICAAC
GLACIERSE
```

38–39

M	S	L	I	B	C
C	B	I	L	S	M
I	M	C	B	L	S
B	L	S	C	M	I
S	I	B	M	C	L
L	C	M	S	I	B

44–45

(maze)

48–49

1 TRAMPLED
4 HOOFED
3 SEASON
5 CROCODILES
7 ARROW
8 GRAZ
9 KENYA
12 NOVEMBER
(FRIDAY, RAINY)

52–53

s	e	n	d
s	e	n	t
v	e	n	t
v	e	s	t
v	a	s	t

56–57

```
CUNIFORMS
AHUWARST W
PZWAGEDEA
TCTMANGMR
IRSEACOPR
VORICFDLI
EPICESSEO
SSRAINKSR
WARLIKEYS
```

58–59

p	r	e	y
p	r	a	y
p	l	a	y
c	l	a	y
c	l	a	w

62–63

R	L	T	E	A	V
A	V	E	L	R	T
L	E	V	A	T	R
T	R	A	V	L	E
E	A	R	T	V	L
V	T	L	R	E	A

66–67

G	E	I	S	H	W
S	H	G	W	E	I
I	W	H	E	S	G
W	S	E	I	G	H
E	G	W	H	I	S
H	I	S	G	W	E

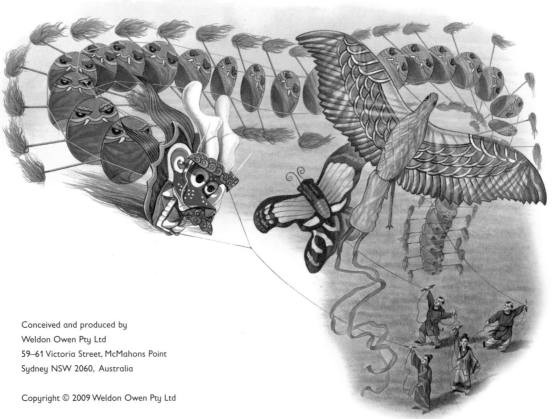

Conceived and produced by
Weldon Owen Pty Ltd
59–61 Victoria Street, McMahons Point
Sydney NSW 2060, Australia

Copyright © 2009 Weldon Owen Pty Ltd

BONNIER BOOKS
Group Publisher John Owen

WELDON OWEN PTY LTD
Chief Executive Officer Sheena Coupe
Creative Director Sue Burk
Associate Publisher Helen Bateman
Senior Vice President, International Sales Stuart Laurence
Vice President Sales: United States and Canada Amy Kaneko
Vice President Sales: Asia and Latin America Dawn Low
Administration Manager, International Sales Kristine Ravn
Publishing Coordinator Gina Belle

Concept Design Kathryn Morgan
Designer Juliana Titin
Art Manager Trucie Henderson

Production Manager Todd Rechner
Production Coordinators Lisa Conway, Mike Crowton

Illustration and Photo Credits
Cover Christa Hook
5 Tony Pyrzakowski, 7 Richard Bonson, 9 Steve
Roberts/ The Art Agency, 11 Darren Pattenden,
13 Guy Troughton and Andrew Davis, 15 John Richards,
17 Malcolm Godwin, 19 Map Illustrations, 21bl and bc
iStock, 21 br and cr Shutterstock, 23 Lynette Cook,
24 Jon Gittoes, 25 David Kirshner, 27 Richard McKennar,
29 Chris Forsey, 31 Christa Hook, 33 Iain McKellar,
34 Martin Camm, 37 Chris Forsey, 38 Ray Grinaway,
39 Corel Corp., 40 Ray Grinaway, 41bl Myke Taylor, 41c
Map Illustrations, 41br Ray Grinaway, 42bl and bc Steve
Roberts/ The Art Agency, 42br Ray Grinaway,
43 Steve Roberts/ The Art Agency, 45 Christa Hook,
47 Oliver Rennert, 49 Trevor Ruth, 51 Chris Forsey,
53 iStock, 55 John Richards, 57 Sally Launder, 59 Christer
Eriksson, 61 Rod Westblade, 63 Steve Trevaskis, 64 and
65 John Richards, 67 David Kirshner

This edition created exclusively for Barnes & Noble, Inc under
ISBN: 978-1-4114-2793-8

Printed in Singapore by Craft Print International Ltd

A WELDON OWEN PRODUCTION